Who Were the Magi?

Lyn Benson

Illustrated by Joshua Benson

Who Were the Magi?

by Lyn Benson
Illustrated by Joshua Benson

For information regarding Joshua Benson art products contact:

Joshua Benson
917-640-0217
www.joshuabenson.com

Design and production by Lyn Benson.

ISBN-10: 0-615-13524-2 • ISBN-13: 978-0-615-13524-3
Printed in the United States of America

Who Were the Magi?

Lyn Benson

Illustrated by Joshua Benson

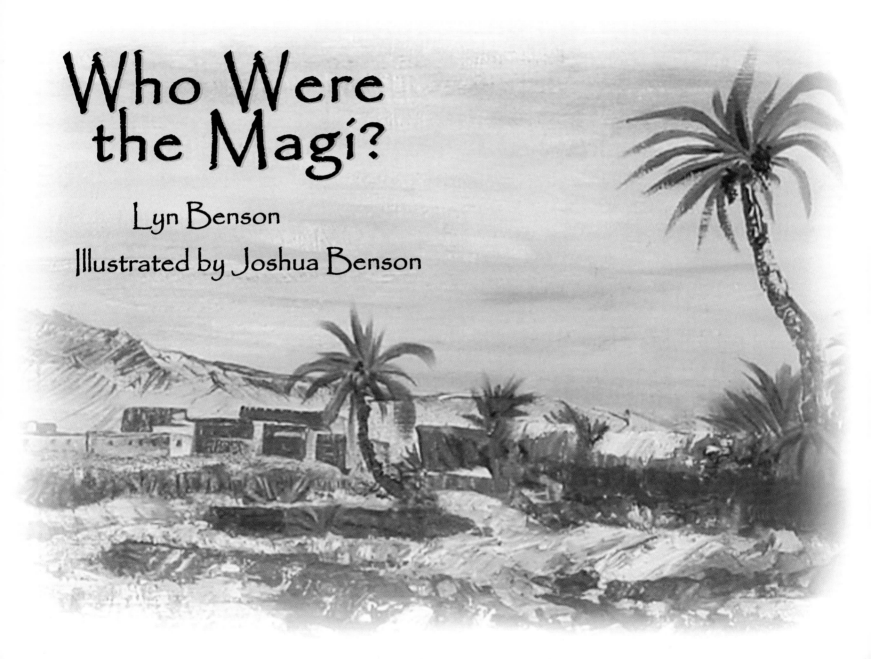

In the beginning God created the heavens and the earth.
And God said, "Let there be lights in the expanse of the sky
... and let them serve as signs ...."
The heavens declare the glory of God; the skies proclaim the work of his hands.
Their voice goes out into all the earth, their words to the ends of the world.
Genesis 1:1,14; Psalm 19:1,4

In the beginning was the Word, and the Word was with God, and the Word was God.
Through him all things were made .... The Word became flesh and made his dwelling among us.
John 1:1,3,14

Therefore the Lord himself will give you a sign: The virgin will be with child
and will give birth to a son, and will call him Immanuel [God with us].
Isaiah 7:14

But you, Bethlehem Ephrathah, ... out of you will come for me one who will be ruler over Israel,
whose origins are from old, from ancient times.
Micah 5:2

After Jesus was born in Bethlehem in Judea, during the time of King Herod,
Magi from the east came to Jerusalem and asked,
"Where is the one who has been born king of the Jews?
We saw his star in the east
and have come to worship him."
Matthew 2:1-2

The young boy watched with a mixture of pride and sadness as his father packed the last bag on his horse. He already missed his daddy, who was a captain in the cavalry of the King of Parthia.

The Parthian Empire had spread to the East from ancient Babylon, while the Roman Empire had risen in the West. Rome had tried to subdue Parthia, but the Parthians had bravely withstood the Romans.

The horse eyed his master and stomped with anticipation, for he had carried him through many battles.

The man turned toward his son, lifted him up into his arms, held him in a lingering hug, and then, with a loud groan, gently set him down.

He held his son's shoulders as he knelt down to meet his eyes and told him, "I will not be fighting this time, my son. This is a very special mission — my men and I will be protecting the caravan of the Magi, who are traveling to a distant land."

His father's eyes filled with tears, knowing he would not see his son again for many months.

In another part of the city, a young man strolled with his father through the bustling streets. Excitement filled the air as they approached the caravan.

"Father, is it true that our journey could take months to reach our destination?"

"Yes, my son, and that will give us much time for you to learn the secrets of our fathers and to understand the reason we make this journey."

His father was one of the Magi, the ruling tribe of priests and government officials who served as the king's Wise Men.

For centuries, kings were surrounded by the most enlightened and wisest men of the land, who were also the religious leaders.

The Parthian Magi had risen in power not only to advise kings, but also to crown kings, or to depose them. The Magi were revered as king makers, for the fates of kings lay in their hands.

"Son, we have discovered a new, mysterious light in the sky — the sign of the birth of a long awaited king in the land of Israel. Our purpose is to find him and to worship him."

"Worship him? Father, why travel so far just to worship a child? Will we not appoint him king when we find him? What about the Roman king on the throne now?"

"Son, this child is no ordinary king that we could appoint. He has been sent from the heavens."

The young man felt a sense of awe as he wondered why the Magi would leave their life as wealthy dignitaries to face months of scorching heat and biting windstorms in the barren desert.

He was thrilled to be included in the company of such important and powerful men, as they took their places among the camels, carts, and horses.

He eagerly waited to hear more of their story as they traveled together. At the end of their journey, he would be one of them, a seeker of this child.

3

As the caravan began to move forward, those
who were gathered to see them off stepped back
to make way for their departure.

Amid the shouts of farewells and blessings, the
caravan made its way to the edge of the city toward
the ancient trade route known as the Silk Road.

The young man watched the city grow distant and faint, until
it finally slipped out of sight. In front of him was the vast barrenness
of the desert.

He felt its mystery as he gazed at the swirls of sand carved by many winds.
The first day grew into the first week, then into months, as the rhythm of travel
settled upon each traveler, swaying with each movement of his animal.

There would be oases along the route where they would stop to refresh themselves and their beasts, and to gather new supplies of food for their journey.

As they pushed forward, they exchanged great stories of times past, pouring over the signs and ancient writings that had beckoned them to make this journey, spurring each other on toward their common goal.

The young man listened intently to them, for he would take his place in the assembly of the Magi when his training was completed.

"Father, what does the land of Israel have to do with us? And this Jewish king — will he rule over us one day?"

"My son, it all began with a young prince who was being educated to take his place among Judah's rulers, a youth just like you.

His name was Daniel..."

So his father began to unfold the story of
Daniel and how they came to make this journey, as he
took him back to the lands of ancient Babylonia and Israel...

"Six hundred years ago," his father began, "there arose a mighty king who had conquered many nations as they fell under his sword.

He was the great King Nebuchadnezzar who reigned over the Babylonian Empire.

But that was not enough for him.

"As the King sought to conquer new lands, he set his eyes on Jerusalem, the capital city of the region in Israel known as Judah.

"The nation of Israel had once been great and was known throughout the world for its worship of only one God, and its magnificent temple built by King Solomon, the richest and wisest man on earth — wiser, even, than all the Wise Men of the East.

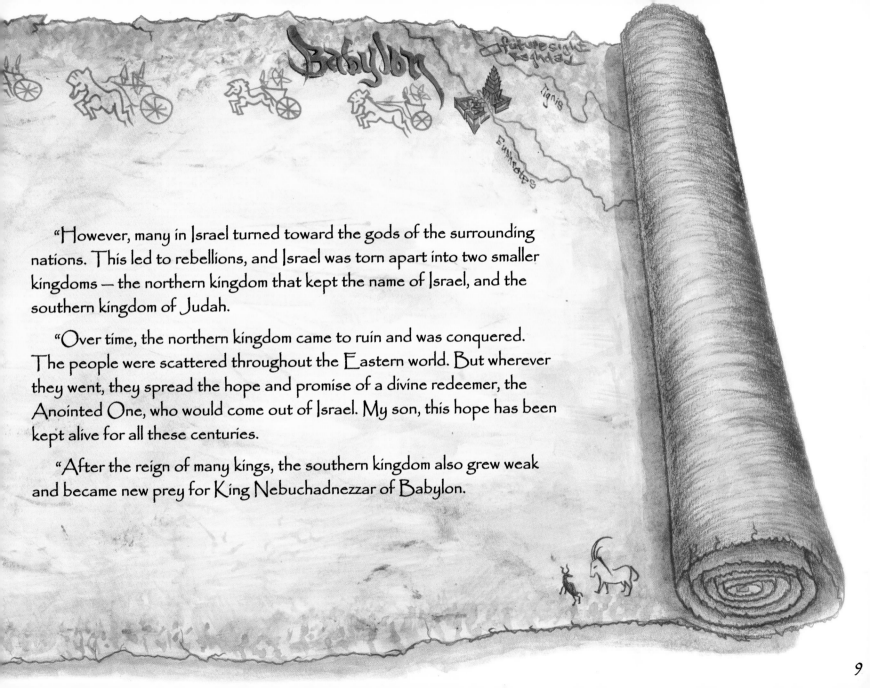

"However, many in Israel turned toward the gods of the surrounding nations. This led to rebellions, and Israel was torn apart into two smaller kingdoms — the northern kingdom that kept the name of Israel, and the southern kingdom of Judah.

"Over time, the northern kingdom came to ruin and was conquered. The people were scattered throughout the Eastern world. But wherever they went, they spread the hope and promise of a divine redeemer, the Anointed One, who would come out of Israel. My son, this hope has been kept alive for all these centuries.

"After the reign of many kings, the southern kingdom also grew weak and became new prey for King Nebuchadnezzar of Babylon.

"Daniel was a prince in the court of Judah
when Nebuchadnezzar's army laid siege to Jerusalem.
His life was about to change forever, as well as
the course of our fathers' lives.

"He and other young men from the royal family and nobility were taken captive and carried off to Babylon, where they would be educated in the royal court.

"They were to learn the language, culture, and religion of Babylon, and then take their places in the council of our fathers, the king's Wise Men. Nebuchadnezzar had gathered the best men from every nation he conquered to add to his royal advisors.

"Daniel was destined to become the wisest of all the Wise Men in Babylon.

"In those days, Babylon was the center of the highest learning in the Eastern world. Our fathers were skilled in all scientific and religious knowledge, and they had served many kings as official court astrologers, magicians, and sorcerers. They had become experts in the knowledge of the natural world, that they might control the unseen spirits of the supernatural world, who determined the course of all nature and the lives of all men.

"People lived in such fear of them that they made images of them to gain their favor. They worshipped these idols as gods, as many people still do today."

"But father," the young man interrupted, "how did we come to worship only one God when most people today still worship the gods of our fathers? When did our fathers change their minds? And why?"

"My son, our fathers did not look at the natural and supernatural worlds as separate from each other. As they increased their vast knowledge of astronomy, they perfected their craft in astrology. As they mastered their understanding of nature, they excelled in the arts of magic. As they accomplished great skill in medicine, they became masters of sorcery.

It was Daniel who changed their minds.

"Although Daniel learned about the Babylonian gods, he refused to worship them and even stood against kings about it. This got him into much trouble at times — even to the point of near execution. But he stood his ground and never forgot the God of Israel.

As our fathers watched Daniel's life and how his God rescued him, they grew to love and admire him — and his God. They were profoundly influenced by him.

"As Daniel grew in wisdom and understanding — even beyond all the Wise Men of Babylon — he rose in favor with the king. Daniel always professed that it was his God who imparted his wonderful skill.

"Our fathers were known among the Wise Men as the wisest men of all. In addition to their great knowledge, the Magi were also skilled in the interpretation of dreams, which they believed were warnings from their gods. Still today, we are blessed with that skill.

"Although they were the king's advisors, the Magi of that day did not have the power over kings that we have today. They were at the mercy of the king's whims, and they could lose their lives at the king's command. That came close to happening under Nebuchadnezzar, but Daniel and his God saved their lives."

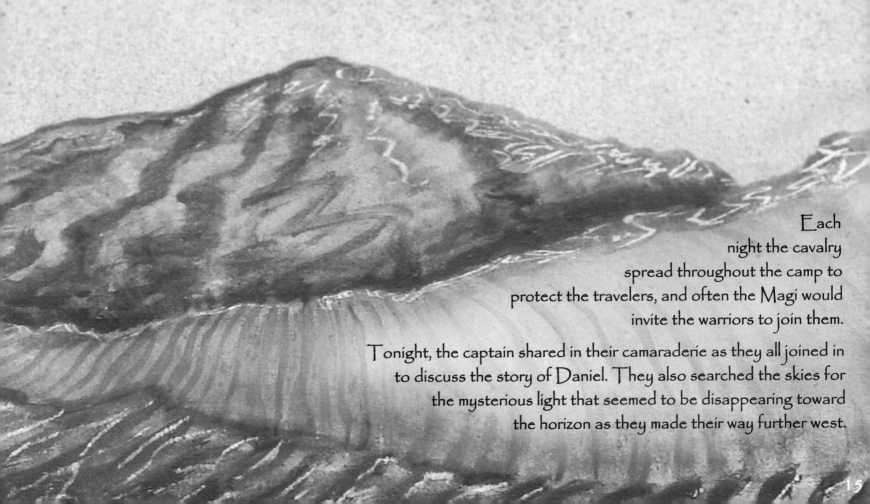

The young man had begun to feel a kinship with Daniel and wanted to hear more, but it was time to stop for the night. The sun was setting on the edge of the desert as the shadows lengthened into dusk. By nightfall, the caravan had set up camp, and campfires dotted the landscape as small groups gathered to share the evening meal.

Each night the cavalry spread throughout the camp to protect the travelers, and often the Magi would invite the warriors to join them.

Tonight, the captain shared in their camaraderie as they all joined in to discuss the story of Daniel. They also searched the skies for the mysterious light that seemed to be disappearing toward the horizon as they made their way further west.

15

During the course of their travel, the captain had come to know the young man and his father. He leaned toward the older man and observed, "You have a fine son, sir. I, too, have a son, a young child, and I hope for the day when he follows in my footsteps as your son follows in yours."

The older father glanced toward his own son, then turned toward the younger father and placed his hand on the warrior's shoulder. He said with admiration, "I'm sure he will, captain. I'm sure he will."

The young man soon felt a oneness with the Magi as he listened to their words. The more they included him, the more he felt drawn into their world. He was beginning to feel he was a part of their history, which was now becoming his own.

His heart was kindled with the wonder and mystery of their mission.

As the fire crackled amid the calls of jackals piercing the night air, the Magi discussed the dangers that faced Daniel as he served King Nebuchadnezzar.

"So how did Daniel save the Magi in Babylon?" the young man eagerly asked.

The other Magi were just as eager to continue the story...

"One night,
a night like this,
the king had a
troubling dream.
It caused him
such distress that
he summoned all
the Wise Men to
interpret the dream —
and also to tell him
what the dream was.

"They replied,
'No man on earth
could do such a
thing — no king
had ever asked
this of any
magician,
enchanter,
or astrologer —
only the gods
could reveal it,
and they do not
live among men.'

"At that, Nebuchadnezzar became furious and ordered the execution of every Wise Man in Babylon, including Daniel.

However, Daniel asked the king for more time to interpret his dream. Since Nebuchadnezzar had grown to admire and trust Daniel, he granted his request.

"Daniel went to his friends and told them what had happened. All their lives were at stake, and they prayed earnestly for God's mercy.

"This was not the last time they would face this kind of danger.

20

"That night, God gave Daniel a vision of a huge statue with a head of gold, chest and arms of silver, belly and thighs of bronze, legs of iron, and feet of iron mixed with baked clay. Finally, a large rock destroyed the statue and grew into a huge mountain that filled the whole earth.

"The next day, he went before the king. As he described the dream, he spoke with boldness and clarity: 'There is a God in heaven who reveals mysteries and has shown you what will happen in days to come. In your dream you saw the rise and fall of four world empires that will be replaced by God's final kingdom on earth.

God has made you ruler over the first empire in this dream. You, O king, are the head of gold.'

The king was stunned. He fell upon his face and paid homage to Daniel. He then promoted Daniel to be head over all the Magi and second ruler over all of Babylon.

Daniel had saved all our fathers' lives.

"Now that Daniel held such a high position, he was able to unfold the Hebrew Scriptures to our fathers, and they came to believe in his God. He also shared many secrets, dreams, and visions with them, which our fathers have carefully preserved through the centuries.

"In one vision, an angel told him when the Anointed One would be revealed — from the decree to rebuild Jerusalem, there would be a certain number of years. And then he would be cut off, but not for himself."

"That part of the vision is a mystery to us," another traveler interrupted. "How could one who has been prophesied and awaited for so long be executed? And not even for his own crime — it makes no sense."

One man, who had been staring into the campfire, looked up in the flickering light and proposed, "This mystery will be revealed to us at some time in the future. But Daniel's vision and Nebuchadnezzar's dream both point to this present time — that the time of his appearing is upon us."

"While Daniel was still living, the great King Cyrus proclaimed that the exiles could return to Jerusalem to rebuild their temple, but not their city. It was not until nearly a century later when another Persian king issued the decree to rebuild the city of Jerusalem.

"For our fathers, the countdown had begun...

"It is only now that we have begun to look for the sign of this long awaited king. For we have been studying the old calendars, and they tell us his time is at hand. Also, we are living in the fourth empire of this dream.

Babylon was overthrown by the Medes and Persians, who were conquered by the Greeks under Alexander the Great. Now Rome has taken over the world — or most of it," he said with a wry smile.

BABYLON   MEDES-PERSIA

"There are no more world kingdoms left in the king's dream. Could this be the dawn of the final kingdom?

"When the new light in the heavens appeared, we knew it had to be his sign. This is what kindled our hearts to seek this child."

Thus ended the story of their beloved prophet Daniel.

The young man's heart burned within him. He couldn't wait to arrive in Jerusalem.

GRƐƐCƐ

ROME

25

After many months and many stories of times past, the caravan finally inched toward Jerusalem. The travelers were weary, but their hearts took on new life as they approached the city. Their anticipation mounted as they went through the gates.

Crowds gathered as the entourage of the Magi entered the city, escorted by their military cavalry.

The young man expected everyone to be as excited as he was. He was not prepared for what he saw.

Each person eyed them with suspicion. The people of Jerusalem were accustomed to caravans arriving with goods to trade, but a caravan full of Magi? And from Parthia? Why were they here? These were warriors and king-makers.

Since Israel was caught in the middle between the two clashing empires, would there be more war with Rome? Would they depose King Herod, whom Rome had placed on the throne of Israel?

Attempting to calm their fears, the Magi began to ask them, "Where is the one who has been born King of the Jews? We saw his star in the east and have come to worship him."

Although the Magi held the power to crown kings, they would not be crowning this one, because his was not to be an earthly kingdom. But nobody in Jerusalem knew that.

When news of their arrival reached King Herod, he was greatly disturbed. The entire city of Jerusalem became stirred up and distressed.

"Scribes! Priests!" Herod called for the teachers of the Hebrew Scriptures. He demanded, "Where is the Jewish Messiah to be born?"

They quickly, but reluctantly, answered him, "In Bethlehem, sire. The prophet Micah wrote, 'out of Bethlehem will come a ruler who will be the shepherd of my people Israel.'"

Herod secretly sent for the Magi to find out more.

The Magi rode in silence under the night sky as they approached the palace of King Herod. The horses snorted and shook their manes as their masters strove to control them.

The young man peered through the dark streets to the small crowd that had gathered when they heard the clang of horses' hooves on the quiet late-night streets. He rode with guarded attention and observed the dread and mistrust on their moonlit faces.

He leaned toward his father and whispered, "Why are they so afraid of us?"

"My son, they do not believe the intent of our journey, that this time we come in peace. But, my son, they have much more to fear from Herod than from us."

"What is that, father?"

"You will know, my son, before long just how much Herod is to be feared."

Herod was waiting
as the Magi neared the
palace. "Hail, King
Herod. We come
looking for the
newborn King
of the Jews."

A look of horror crossed Herod's face for just an instant, but he quickly produced a large smile, opened his arms in greeting, and hurriedly received them into the palace.

After finding out when the star had first appeared, Herod said with seductive earnestness, "Go to Bethlehem and search carefully for the child. Report back to me so I, too, may go and worship him."

The Magi departed from Jerusalem and headed for Bethlehem.

The young man was perplexed and asked his father, "Why is this such a secret? If this is the promised Messiah we have heard so much about, why don't the people of Jerusalem also want to find the one we seek?"

"My son, they may not know the prophecies. Perhaps their religious leaders are afraid of what Herod would do if they made them known. Or perhaps they do not hold Daniel's words to their hearts as we do.

"I have heard they do not believe that the prophecies are for this time. Or perhaps the people have much to fear if they accompany us. This is truly a mystery, but perchance we will understand it some day."

That day was to come very soon.

Suddenly the light from heaven they had seen in the east reappeared.

"Look!" they all cried out with excitement. They dismounted their animals with exuberance and began to jump up and down, hugging each other with tears of joy they had never felt before.

Their droopy-eyed camels looked on, half smiling in bored acceptance of their masters' jubilation.

Along their way toward Bethlehem, the Magi learned from dwellers of that area that Caesar Augustus had recently called for a census of the entire Roman world, and people from all over had to travel to the place of their family lineage.

With furtive eyes, they recounted the story. "The child you seek was born in a stable there, because the inn was full. On that night, we heard that shepherds nearby had been visited by angels who announced his birth to them. They found the baby in a stable, just as the angels had said. They've been spreading this news all over the area ever since."

By now, time had passed since the child's birth. The light went ahead of the Magi and finally rested over a house where the child and his parents now dwelled.

"My son, this light reminds me of the light in the stories of when the Israelites escaped from their slavery in Egypt long, long ago, for it went ahead of them, just as it is doing now."

When the Magi came into the presence
of the child with his mother Mary, and Joseph,
their hearts were moved with awe as they
began to sense the quiet wonder of God's
favor on mankind.

They bowed with deep reverence,
hesitated a moment, and then opened their
treasures to present him with gifts of
gold, frankincense, and myrrh.

The three gifts they gave him foretold
the purpose of his life...

They gave him gold, for this was the gift given to kings... he would one day be the King of Kings, the Shepherd of his people.

They gave him frankincense, for this was the holy fragrance used by the priests in the temple offerings and sacrifices... he was to be the mediator between God and man.

They gave him myrrh, the oil of burial, for he was to be cut off — executed — but not for himself... he was to sacrifice his life as a ransom for the sins of the world.

37

Early the next morning, the young man's father came to him with startling news.

"My son, there are those of us who have had a dream. We have been warned to return home by a different route and not to return to Herod. After taking counsel together, we have decided to go in the opposite direction and not return to Jerusalem. I fear there is danger in Herod's plans."

Mary and her husband Joseph were awed and honored by the visit of the Magi. They saw them off on their journey home with waves of farewell and Godspeed.

After the Magi left, Joseph also had a dream in which he was warned to take the child to Egypt to escape Herod, who had purposed in his heart to kill the child and had sought to use the Magi to find him.

What happened next, as a result of their visit, they could have never imagined.

39

When Herod found out he had been outwitted by the Magi, he was furious, and he ordered his soldiers to kill every boy in Bethlehem under the age of two.

That night, the soldiers swept through the town and murdered every baby boy. As they went from house to house, horrified screaming pierced the night in the once-peaceful streets.

The sound of uncontrolled wailing echoed for days.

The bitter sorrow in Bethlehem had been prophesied many years
before, by the prophet Jeremiah, when he wrote these words:

"A voice is heard in Ramah, weeping and
great mourning, Rachel weeping for her children
and refusing to be comforted, because
they are no more."

When news reached the Magi about what had happened in Bethlehem, the joy they had felt only days before turned into horrified grief. They wept for those who had lost their children to Herod's wrath.

The young man's father drew him close and hugged his neck, crying with sorrow, and yet with hope. "My son," he said through his tears, "There will always be evil men. What this king has done is unthinkable. But although he tried, Herod could not stop the coming of the Redeemer, whom God had promised throughout the Hebrew Scriptures. There is yet hope for all of us, my son, and we will know some day why all this happened."

But in his heart, a gnawing question whispered — did our coming here cause this to happen? — Should we have gone back to Herod as planned? He carried this regret throughout his years, and it haunted him until his final day.

He looked at his son intently. "No matter what other men might do or say, always remember what we felt in our hearts when we found him."

When the captain heard what the Romans had done, his heart filled with rage. He called out with vengeance, "We must go back to avenge these children." His heart grieved as he thought of his own young son who would have perished if he had been born at this time in Bethlehem.

"No," the Magi determined after reasoning together, "we have done enough here. Let us continue homeward." With sorrowful hearts they looked east and set their faces toward home.

43

Three decades later...

The young man had taken his father's place in the court of the Magi. Word had spread throughout Israel and the Roman Empire, and now had reached Parthia, that a popular rabbi had arisen, whom the people hoped would redeem Israel from the Roman Empire.

He had ridden into Jerusalem on a donkey, hailed by the people as their king. However, within a few days, he was executed — but then had risen from the dead! His followers, who were multiplying throughout the world, proclaimed that the purpose for his coming was to die as a sacrifice to redeem all people.

"Aha!" the Magi shouted aloud as their faces shone with sudden understanding. "This must be the one we sought so long ago. Now the mystery that has perplexed us all this time finally has meaning."

The young man, now much older, felt new joy rise in his heart.
If only he could share this good news with his father. He went
to his father's grave and knelt down.

"After all these years of wondering, father — oh, that you
could share the comfort and joy that is mine today." As he
wept, he somehow sensed that his father already knew,
and that one day they would again embrace with
the same joy they had shared together that
fateful night, when the light from heaven
led them to the child for whom
they had searched.

The Magi could finally rest assured
that the greatest healer of human
hearts had come, no matter who tried
to stop him. Their journey of so
many years ago was truly a gift
from their beloved Daniel,
whose prophecies they had
preserved for nearly six
centuries had finally
come to pass.

In another part of the city, a youth ran with his father to tell his grandfather the good news. His father was in the king's cavalry, just as his grandfather had been.

The old captain's face broke into a wide smile when he heard their words.

With new life in his heart, he beckoned to his grandson, "Sit down, young man. I have a long story to tell you. Your father was only a young boy when I left on a faraway journey..."

The young man loved to hear this story every time his grandfather told it.

Only this time, it was different...

Rejoice greatly, O Daughter of Zion! ... See, your king comes to you,
righteous and having salvation, gentle and riding on ... the foal of a donkey.
Zechariah 9:9

For we do not have a high priest who is unable to sympathize with our weaknesses,
but we have one who has been tempted in every way, just as we are —
yet was without sin.
Hebrews 4:15

... For he was cut off from the land of the living;
for the transgression of my people he was stricken.
Isaiah 53:8

... I lay down my life — only to take it up again. No one takes it from me,
but I lay it down of my own accord ....
John 10:17-18

And beginning with Moses and all the Prophets, he explained to them
what was said in all the Scriptures concerning himself ....
"Were not our hearts burning within us while he talked with us on the road
and opened the Scriptures to us?"
Luke 24:27,32

49

Scriptures on Which This Story Is Based